TEDDY BEAR
COUNTING

Barbara Barbieri McGrath
***Illustrated by* Tim Nihoff**

SCHOLASTIC INC.
New York Toronto London Auckland
Sydney Mexico City New Delhi Hong Kong

To Judy O'Malley, for bearing with me—B. B. M.

To my big sister, Debi, the one
you can always count on—T. N.

Text copyright © 2010 by Barbara Barbieri McGrath.
Illustrations copyright © 2010 by Tim Nihoff.
All rights reserved. Published by Scholastic Inc., 557 Broadway, New York, NY 10012, by arrangement with Charlesbridge Publishing, Inc. SCHOLASTIC and associated logos are trademarks and/or registered trademarks of Scholastic Inc.

First Scholastic printing, October 2010

Illustrations hand drawn digitally in Adobe Photoshop
Display type set in Animated Gothic and text type set in Century Schoolbook
Designed by Susan Mallory Sherman

ISBN 978-0-545-30840-3

12 11 10 9 8 7 6 5 4 3 2   12 13 14 15/0

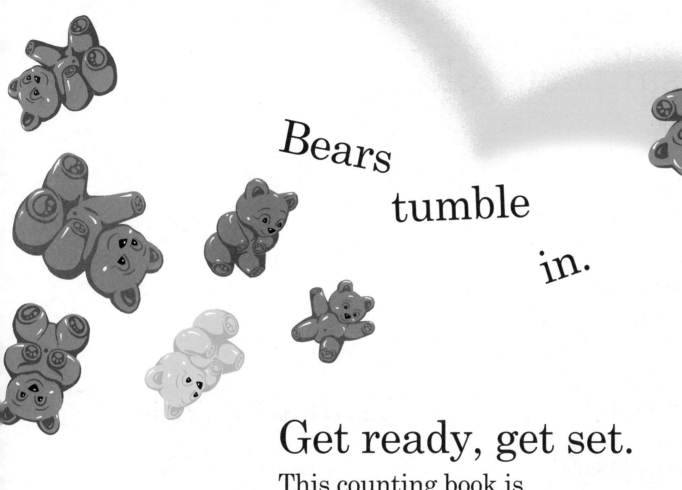

Bears tumble in.

Get ready, get set.
This counting book is
the most playful yet!

Bears say their colors.

It's easy to do.

"I'm red!" "And I'm yellow!"

"I'm green!"

"Well, I'm blue!"

1

First is one red.

Yellow makes two.

2

A green bear is three.

Count four with this blue.

4

One red marches in

5

to make five bears in all.

When yellow joins, too,

six teddies sit tall.

A green one arrives.

Seven now form a group.

Then a blue comes along,

making eight in the troop.

8

One bear cartwheels in

to make nine in the line.

9

Another drops by,
and ten teddies look fine.

10

Ten teddies line up,
then bend low to bow.

11

To count to eleven
add one teddy now.

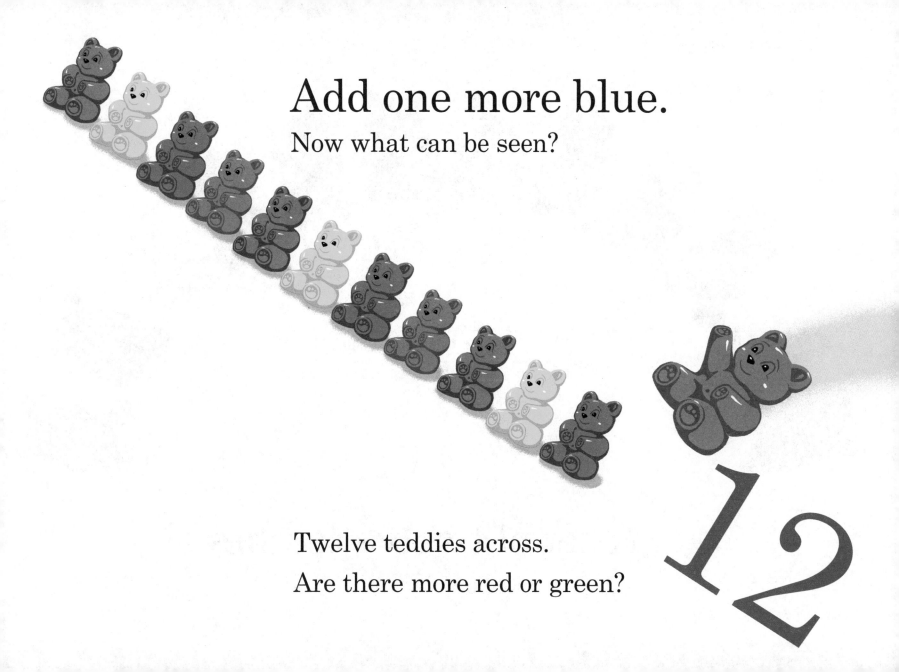

Add one more blue.
Now what can be seen?

Twelve teddies across.
Are there more red or green?

12

A set of twelve teddies

makes a rainbow for you.

Six bears can choose partners—

$$2+2+2+2+2+2=12$$

that's six sets of two.

The bears move around

and make three sets of four.

Count up how many:

just twelve and no more.   4+4+4=12

Teddies all dancing

make four sets of three,
and still only twelve
are all we can see.

$$3+3+3+3=12$$

Two sets of six say,
"How do you do?"

6+6=12

Since that went so well,
they try something new.

Bears hop,

skip, and jump,

and fly through the air.
When they all land
they make a big square.

The bears shape a circle

that goes round and round.

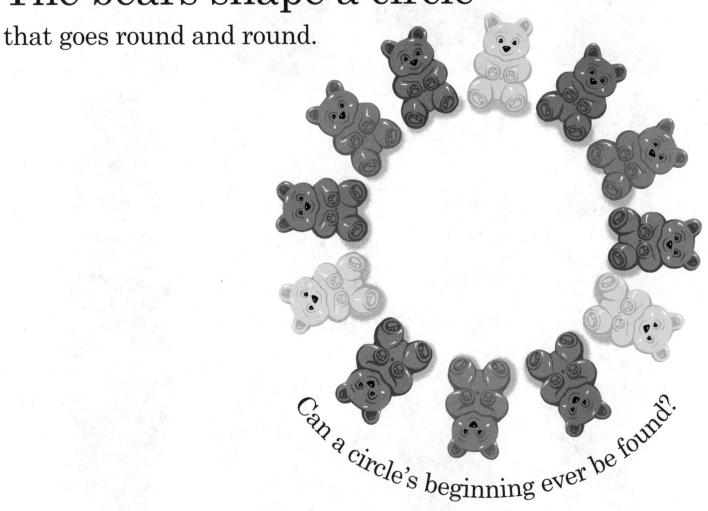

Can a circle's beginning ever be found?

A triangle's next

before these bears stop.

They give it three sides, with one bear on the top!

One bear of each color

won't risk being late.

Four bears have to go.

That leaves only eight.

$$12-4=8$$

More teddies are leaving.

It's bear moving day.

With places to go,

two more walk away.

$$8-2=6$$

Six bears remain

with little to do.

Say so long to four. . . .

We're left with just two.

 $6-4=2$

One little teddy

runs away fast.

Say hello to the bear
who chose to be last.

$2-1=1$

The bear stands alone.

What a brave little hero.

When he trots away,

there are none. That means zero!

0

$$1-1=0$$

Bye, counting bears.

They're gone now, but when
the teddies come back,   they'll   all   play   again!

The bears had great fun. They tried something new.
To help them remember, let's have a review!

COLORS

red

yellow

green

blue

SHAPES

square

circle

triangle

NUMBERS

1	one	5	five	9	nine
2	two	6	six	10	ten
3	three	7	seven	11	eleven
4	four	8	eight	12	twelve

SETS OF TWELVE

1 set

2 sets

3 sets

4 sets

6 sets